This book belongs to:

Name _____

Age _____

Editor: Anne Ewart   Designer: Martin Shubrook

© Disney. Published in Great Britain in 2000 by Egmont
World Ltd., a division of Egmont Holding Ltd., Deanway
Technology Centre, Wilmslow Road, Handforth,
Cheshire SK9 3FB. Printed in Italy. All rights reserved.
ISBN 0 7498 4876 6

£5.99
UK only

contents

Mickey's Christmas Carol
PART 1

It was a cold and snowy Christmas Eve in London. Huge snowflakes were falling from the sky and the whole town was covered with a soft, white blanket of snow. The spirit of Christmas was in the air, and everyone was looking forward to spending Christmas with their friends and families around the Christmas tree...

Everyone... but Ebenezer Scrooge. For Scrooge was a miserable, old miser who hated Christmas. "Bah, humbug!" he muttered, as he walked past a jolly Santa Claus and some happy children singing Christmas carols. To Scrooge, Christmas was just another day and he hurried through the streets to the Counting House, where he worked.

Pushing open the door to the Counting House, Scrooge saw his loyal employee, Bob Cratchitt, adding a lump of coal to the furnace. "And just what do you think you're doing?" bellowed Scrooge. "I was just trying to stay warm, Sir, and to keep the ink in my pen from freezing," replied Cratchitt. "You already used a lump last week," replied Scrooge, "there's no need for using another lump now." Poor Cratchitt was forced to put the lump of coal back and carry on working in the freezing cold.

Scrooge sat behind his huge desk and started to count the piles of gold coins that were neatly stacked around him. "Let's see," mumbled Scrooge, merrily, "the 80% interest on this loan, compounded daily, amounts to...." Scrooge giggled and hugged his big bags of coins. "Oh, money, money, money!" laughed Scrooge.

Suddenly, there was a knock at the office door and Master Fred, Scrooge's nephew, walked in. "Merry Christmas!" cried Master Fred. "What is it that you want?" asked Scrooge, angrily. "To invite you to Christmas dinner, Uncle," replied Master Fred. "There'll be plump goose, chestnut stuffing, plum pudding...."

"You know I can't eat that stuff," barked Scrooge, "now get out of here!" Scrooge gave his nephew a good kick, which sent him flying out of the Counting House and into the snowy street. Master Fred landed with a thud in the deep snow. "I have no use for Christmas," cried Scrooge. "And don't bother coming back!"

Back to front

Mickey and his friends always have fun when they're together! Look at this picture and see if you can find its exact mirror image in one of the pictures below.

a

b

c

d

14

Funny faces

Unscramble the letters in the balls to find six names. Can you match them to each of the funny faces?

i c m e k y

u t p o l

i n i e n m

o n d l a d

o g f y o

a d i y s

Mickey's straw test

Mickey has set a tricky test for you and your friends.

Which four straws do you need to remove so that only eight squares are left in the pattern below?

Answer: The four straws in the middle.

Donald sorts it out

Donald is very proud of all the things he's found at the seaside! Can you help him count up how many sets there are of each group of objects?

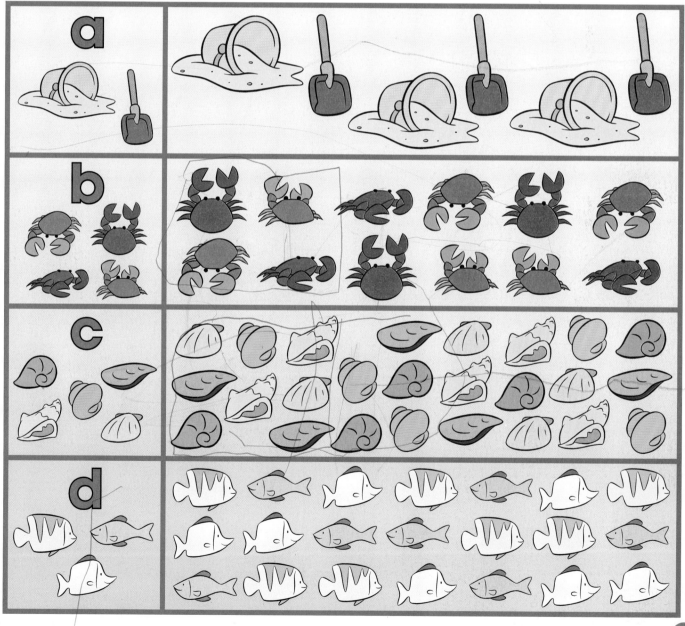

Answers: a, 3. b, 3. c, 5. d, 7.

Mickey's Christmas Carol
PART 2

After Master Fred's interruption, Scrooge returned to his desk. He carried on working until he heard the clocks chime eight. "Hmmm, five minutes fast," said Scrooge, looking at his pocket watch. "Another five minutes to quitting time, Cratchitt," he added. Cratchitt timidly asked Scrooge if he could have half the next day off to celebrate Christmas with his family. "Oh, all right," grumbled Scrooge, "and you can go now, but I'll dock you half a day's fees!" "Yes sir!" replied Cratchitt, leaping excitedly down from his desk.

Eventually, Scrooge too decided it was time to go home. But when Scrooge arrived at his front door, he was shocked to hear his door knocker speak to him. The door knocker looked just like his old partner at the Counting House, Jacob Marley. But it couldn't be. Door knockers didn't talk! Quickly, Scrooge ran into his house and locked the door behind him.

Sitting in his armchair, Scrooge heard a ghostly voice, calling him. "Ebenezer Scroooooooge," it cried. Scrooge turned to see the ghost of Jacob Marley walking towards him, dragging a heavy piggy bank and chains. He could hardly believe his eyes! Scrooge listened fearfully as the ghost explained that he was carrying the chains as a punishment for being so greedy while he was alive. "Tonight you will be visited by three spirits," cried the ghost. "Listen to them, and be sure to mend your greedy ways, or your chains will be even heavier than mine...." With that, the ghost of Jacob Marley left.

"Nonsense," thought Scrooge, as he climbed into bed. "There is no such thing as spirits." But, while Scrooge slept, a little figure with an umbrella came into his room. Scrooge woke with a start. "Who are you?" asked Scrooge, staring at the small visitor. "I am the Ghost of Christmas Past," replied the little spirit, showing Scrooge his badge.

The spirit told Scrooge to grab hold and hang on tight. "Where are we going?" asked Scrooge. "We're going to visit your past," said the spirit. He opened his umbrella and carried Scrooge out of the window and into the snowy night. They swirled through the sky and glided over the rooftops, with Scrooge hanging on to the little spirit for dear life!

Soon, they landed beside a lively dance hall. Scrooge and the spirit looked in through the window and saw all of Scrooge's old friends from the past, making music, dancing and having a wonderful time. Suddenly, Scrooge spotted himself in the middle of the dance floor, whirling around with the lovely Isabel. "Why, that's me!" he said to the little spirit. "Oh, how I loved her," Scrooge murmured, fondly. "Yes," said the spirit, "but in ten years' time, you learned to love something far more. Remember?"

Scrooge remembered how one day, while sitting in his Counting House, the lovely Isabel had come to visit. Scrooge was more interested in his money than Isabel and he remembered how she had left the Counting House, broken-hearted and in tears. "You see?" explained the spirit. "You loved your money more than that beautiful lady, and so you lost her forever." "Oh please, Spirit, take these terrible memories away from me, I can't bear them!" pleaded Scrooge. But the Ghost of Christmas Past just shook his head. "Scrooge, you made these memories yourself."

Fancy dress mix-up

Goofy has taken lots of photos of his friends at a fancy dress party, but they haven't come out quite as he expected! Can you work out which costumes **Mickey**, **Minnie**, **Donald**, **Daisy** and **Pluto** are wearing?

knight   clown   cheerleader

fireman   film star

Daisy's day out

Daisy is getting ready to go shopping with Minnie. Starting with 'a', follow the word trail alphabetically to Minnie, first with your finger and then with a pen.

action

bright   hat   ice-cream

clothes   gloves   jewels   key

date   extra   friends   luxury

new   mirror   ring

orange   queue   shops

party   treat

umbrella

vogue   xylophone

wink   yoga   zoom

Snow time!

Mickey and his friends are having a fantastic time playing in the snow! Join in their fun by playing this game with your friends.

Splat! Miss a turn.

7

8

start

1

5

9

2

Splat! Miss a turn.

4

14

Splat! Miss a turn.

15

Grab a lift on a sledge! Go forward 5 spaces.

How to play

You will need: a dice and a counter for each player. Take turns to roll the dice. Move your counter forward the number of spaces shown on the dice and follow each of the instructions you land on. The first person to slide their way to the finish is the winner, but watch out for the snowball splats!

23

Splat! Miss a turn.

25

Build a snow camp! Throw again.

Build a fantastic snowman! Throw again.

Splat! Miss a turn.

11

21

27

20

Catch a cold! Go back 5 spaces.

29

19

30

18

finish

Mickey's Christmas Carol

PART 3

After being visited by the Ghost of Christmas Past, Scrooge found himself back in his bed. Suddenly, Scrooge felt a breeze in his room and heard a thundering voice. "Fee, Fi, Fo, Fum!" Scrooge remembered that the ghost of Jacob Marley had said he would be visited by three spirits. This must be the second! Terrified, Scrooge pulled back his curtain and saw a giant sitting beside his bed. The giant was surrounded by the most magnificent food Scrooge had ever seen. "Who are you?" asked Scrooge, shaking with fear. "I am the Ghost of Christmas Present," came the reply. "Oh please," begged Scrooge, "please don't eat me!"

The giant spirit picked Scrooge up and held him, dangling, by his nightshirt. "Me? Eat you? Why would I want to eat a miserable miser like you, when there are so many good things to enjoy?" roared the giant. "What is all this food?" asked Scrooge. "This is the food of generosity, which you have long denied your fellow man," answered the giant. "Bah, generosity. What good is it?" muttered Scrooge. "Let me show you what generosity means to people with much less than you, Ebenezer Scrooge," said the giant.

Carefully, the giant pushed open the roof of Scrooge's house and stepped out into the street. It was late at night and everyone was inside celebrating Christmas. "Where are we going?" cried Scrooge. "You'll see," answered the giant, as he picked Scrooge up and lumbered through the snowy streets of the town.

Soon, Scrooge and the giant came to an old shack. Through the window, they saw a poor family gathered around a table. "Why, it's my employee, Bob Cratchitt!" cried Scrooge. Bob Cratchitt and his family were waiting for their youngest child, little Tim, to reach the table on crutches. "Spirit, what is wrong with that child?" asked Scrooge. "Ah, poor Tim," answered the giant. "I'm afraid that if that little one does not get more to eat, there will be an empty place at the table for Christmas next year." "Oh, Spirit, I didn't know that this was how Cratchitt lived," moaned Scrooge, but the giant had vanished. "Spirit!" cried Scrooge. "Please, I must know what happens to little Tim!"

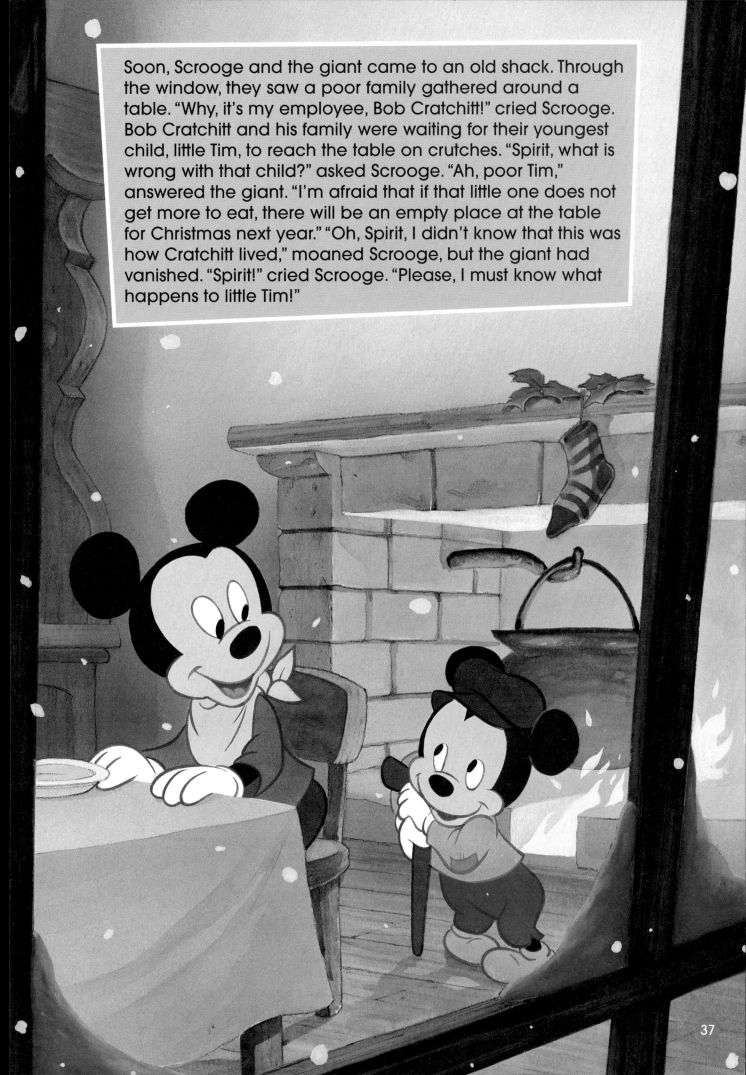

Suddenly, Scrooge was surrounded by a cloud of smoke. When the smoke cleared, Scrooge saw a large, scary shape smoking a fat cigar. "You must be the Ghost of Christmas Future," trembled Scrooge, as he hid behind a tombstone. The large shape did not speak but slowly nodded its head. "What will happen to little Tim Cratchitt?" asked Scrooge.

Without speaking, the spirit pointed towards a small hill, where Scrooge saw a group of mourners gathered around a lonely grave. Looking more closely, Scrooge saw that it was Bob Cratchitt and his family. Scrooge watched as the poor family wept by the grave. "Oh no!" cried Scrooge, "it can't be!" Bob Cratchitt knelt by the grave and placed a crutch against the tombstone. It was the crutch of little Tim! Was it too late? "Spirit! I didn't want things to turn out this way. Tell me there is still time to change them!" cried Scrooge, guiltily.

The spirit didn't answer but turned and walked towards a freshly dug grave. There were no mourners or friends at this grave. The spirit struck a match and held it close to the tombstone. "Ahhh! Oh no!" cried Scrooge. The engraving read: *RIP Ebenezer Scrooge.* Scrooge couldn't believe that he was looking into his very own grave, and that he would be buried there without a friend to bid him farewell. "Ebenezer Scrooge, you'll be the richest man in the grave!!!" bellowed the spirit. With that, the spirit pushed Scrooge into his grave. Scrooge screamed, as he felt himself falling and falling, until he landed with a terrible thump!

Minnie's maze

Minnie is busy collecting flowers. Follow the path that shows the correct spelling for each of the pictures. How many flowers will Minnie collect along the way?

start

bell · belle

beau · bow

eye · i

blew

blue

right · write

sale

sail

sum 2+3 some

finish

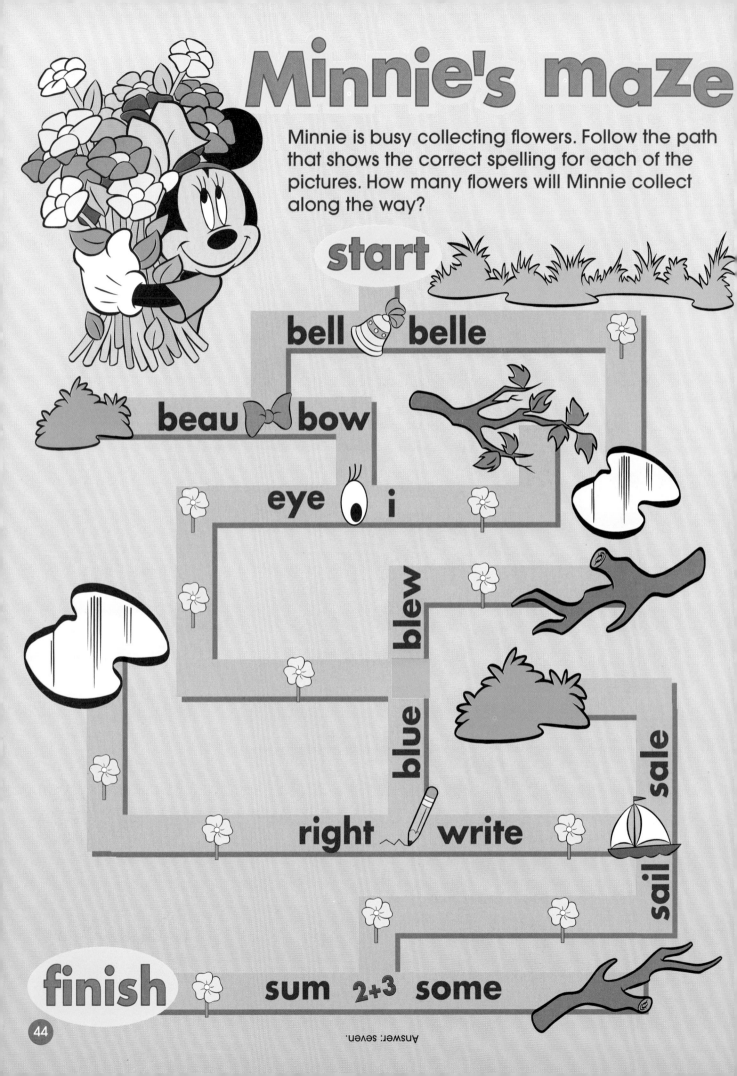

Answer: seven.

Jigsaw jumble

Mickey and Donald have nearly finished their jigsaw puzzle but there are still five pieces left to find. Can you see which pieces they need?

45

Pluto's page

Join in Pluto's playtime by finding the answers to each of these puzzles.

1

Unscramble the letters below and match each of the words to a part of Pluto's body. Then, read the letters on the red lines to find out what Pluto enjoys doing best.

1. **pasw** = ___ ___ ___ ___
2. **atil** = ___ ___ ___ ___
3. **raes** = ___ ___ ___ ___
4. **esye** = ___ ___ ___ ___
5. **hcni** = ___ ___ ___ ___
6. **osen** = ___ ___ ___ ___
7. **gsle** = ___ ___ ___ ___

2 How many frisbees will Pluto catch if he catches all the ones that add up to 9?

3 Pluto's fun never stops, not even when he's sleeping! Can you draw a circle around each of the words that rhyme with the word 'fun'?

play
run
one
done
sun
bone
race

Memory match

Mickey and Minnie are playing a fun game to test their memory. Here's how you and a friend can play too!

How to play

Cover each of the faces with a small piece of paper. Take turns to lift up two pieces of paper at a time. If the faces underneath match each other exactly keep hold of the pieces of paper. If they don't, take a good look and then put the pieces of paper back again. When there are no pieces of paper left to pick up, count how many you've each collected. The player with the most is the winner!

Mickey's Christmas Carol

PART 4

Scrooge thought that he was at the bottom of his own grave, but suddenly, he realised that he was back in his bedroom, struggling under a blanket! Outside, he could hear the church bells chiming and he realised that it was Christmas morning. "It's not too late! I still have one more chance!" cried Scrooge. He grabbed his hat and cane and ran outside! "Merry Christmas!" cried a very happy Scrooge, as he slid down the banister of his steps. He was delighted to be alive and to have one last chance to become a kind and generous man. Scrooge ran through the streets, crying *Merry Christmas* and waving to all the carol singers.

Scrooge spotted his nephew Fred, riding through the town in his horse and buggy. "Merry Christmas, Nephew!" cried Scrooge, running straight out in front of his horse. "I look forward to seeing you at Christmas dinner!" Fred was very confused. "You mean, you're coming?" he asked. "Of course I'm coming, I wouldn't miss that wonderful meal for anything, so keep my plate hot!" replied Scrooge, with a huge smile.

Scrooge's next stop was the home of his faithful employee, Bob Cratchitt. When Cratchitt answered the door, Scrooge pretended to be angry with him. "It's high time you were at work, Christmas or no Christmas," snarled Scrooge. Bob Crachitt tried to remind Scrooge that he had given him half a day off for Christmas. "Bah, humbug!" snorted Scrooge. While Scrooge pretended to be angry, Bob Cratchitt's children sneaked over to have a look in Scrooge's sack. They were amazed to see that it was full of lovely new toys!

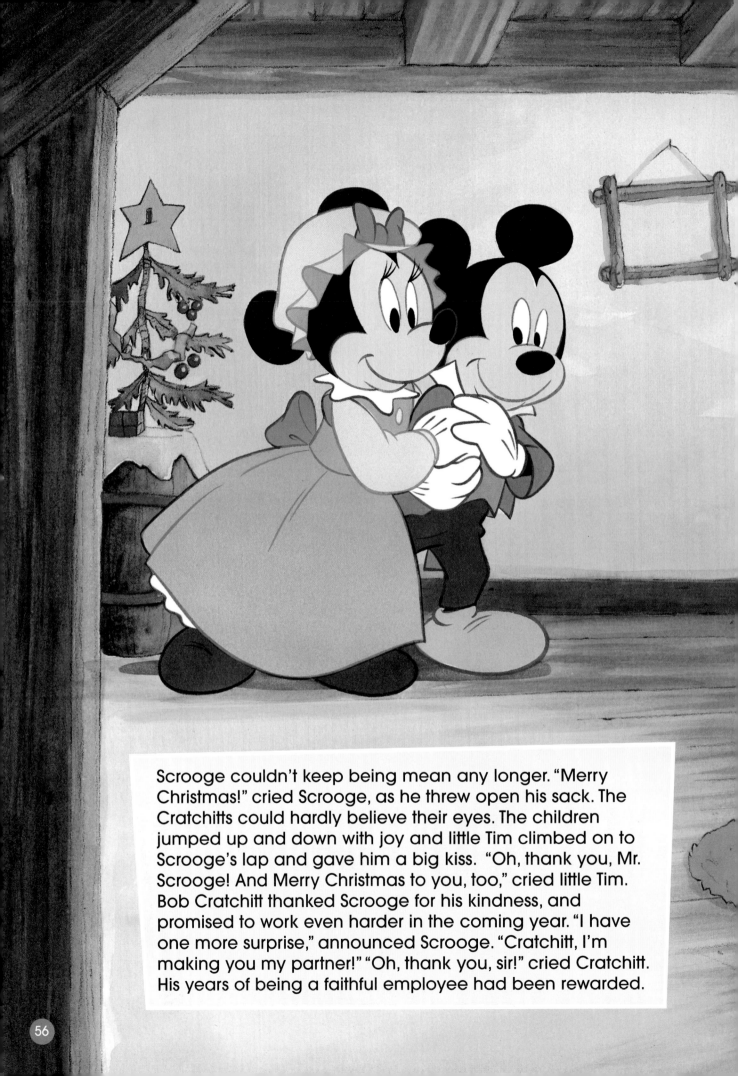

Scrooge couldn't keep being mean any longer. "Merry Christmas!" cried Scrooge, as he threw open his sack. The Cratchitts could hardly believe their eyes. The children jumped up and down with joy and little Tim climbed on to Scrooge's lap and gave him a big kiss. "Oh, thank you, Mr. Scrooge! And Merry Christmas to you, too," cried little Tim. Bob Cratchitt thanked Scrooge for his kindness, and promised to work even harder in the coming year. "I have one more surprise," announced Scrooge. "Cratchitt, I'm making you my partner!" "Oh, thank you, sir!" cried Cratchitt. His years of being a faithful employee had been rewarded.

And so, the miserable miser, Ebenezer Scrooge, learned to be a kind and generous man for the rest of his days and he was never heard to say *Bah, humbug* ever again!

Mickey's quiz

Can you find the answers to Mickey's ten questions?

1) When Scrooge was mean, what was his favourite saying?

2) What did Scrooge love, more than anything else in the world?

3) What was the name of Scrooge's faithful employee?

4) How many minutes fast was the clock in Scrooge's office?

5) What was Master Fred carrying when he visited his uncle?

6) How many spirits did Jacob Marley tell Scrooge he would be visited by?

7) What was the name of the last spirit to visit Scrooge?

8) What was the name of Scrooge's old girlfriend?

9) What does RIP stand for?

10) What is on top of the Cratchitt's Christmas tree?

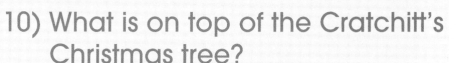

Answers: 1) Bah, humbug. 2) Money 3) Bob Cratchitt. 4) Five. 5) A Christmas wreath. 6) Three. 7) The Ghost of Christmas Future. 8) Isabel. 9) Rest In Peace. 10) A star.

59

You could win a fantastic family break to

Win!  Win!

Visitors young and old can discover the magic of Disneyland® Paris with its Theme Park, its seven themed hotels and of course Disney® Village, the entertainment centre.

The Prize: includes two nights bed and breakfast for a family of four at one of the fabulous Disneyland Paris themed hotels*, plus three days unlimited entry into the Disneyland Park.

2001 will be the best year ever at Disneyland Paris!

In addition to over 50 amazing attractions, rides and shows, this year at Disneyland Paris there will be the most fantastic seasonal festivals for you and your family to enjoy!

The year starts off magically at Disneyland Paris, as from January until March 2001 Kids Go Free to the magic. In March you can enjoy all the craic of the Celtic Festival or salsa the night away in the Festival Latino. Summer is always magical at Disneyland Paris and then before you know it... Trick or Treat! Welcome to HalloweenLand! Then, the following month brings the fantastic Bonfire Spectacular Celebrations. Also from November, until the end of the year, it's the magic of a Very Merry Disney® Christmas all wrapped up at Disneyland Paris just for you!

Come and experience the magic in 2001 at Disneyland Paris
Disneyland Paris, The Magic is Closer Than You Think.
For more information on Disneyland Paris call: 08705 030303
or visit: www.disney.co.uk

How to Enter: Unscramble these letters to spell out the name of Mickey's pet dog : LTPOU

Send your answer, along with your name and address to:

Egmont World Ltd, Deanway Technology Centre, Wilmslow Road, Handforth, Cheshire SK9 3FB.

The closing date for entries is the 12th January 2001.

Terms and conditions

The family break includes accommodation for four – up to two adults and two children (aged 3-11 inclusive) sharing a family room (2 double beds) at one of the Disneyland Paris themed hotels *(excluding The Disneyland® Hotel), plus 2 continental breakfasts and 3 days unlimited entry to the theme park for each person. The prize cannot be modified and there is no cash alternative. The prize is valid from 1 January 2001 for 1 year and is **subject to availability**. Travel insurance is not included, but it is strongly advised that you take some out. Any costs incurred additional to the prize package elements listed (telephone charges, room service etc) are at guests' own expense. Normal Disneyland Paris booking conditions apply. Travel will be by Eurostar, subject to availability. Transport to and from Waterloo station is not included. The prize winner if under 18 must be accompanied by an adult on the winning holiday. One winner will be chosen randomly from the total number of entries from this and four other Disney annuals. The winner will be notified by post. Judges' decision will be final and no correspondence shall be entered into. The winner's name will be made available on request from Egmont World Ltd, Deanway Technology Centre, Wilmslow Road, Handforth, Cheshire, SK9 3FB after 2nd February 2001 - please enclose an SAE. Employees (and their relatives) of Egmont World Ltd and the Walt Disney Company Ltd and their associated companies are not eligible to enter. Entries are limited to one per person. Competition is open to residents of the UK, Ireland and the Channel Islands. The publishers reserve the right to vary prizes, subject to availability.

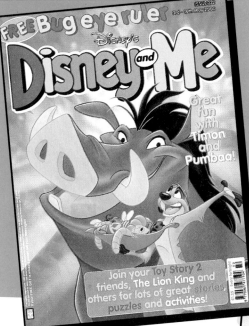